Wh... is Baby?

Story by Julie Ellis
Pictures by Joanne Partis

OXFORD
UNIVERSITY PRESS

Where is baby?

3

I can see jam on the floor.

I can see jam on the door.

I can see jam on the coat.

I can see jam on the bears.

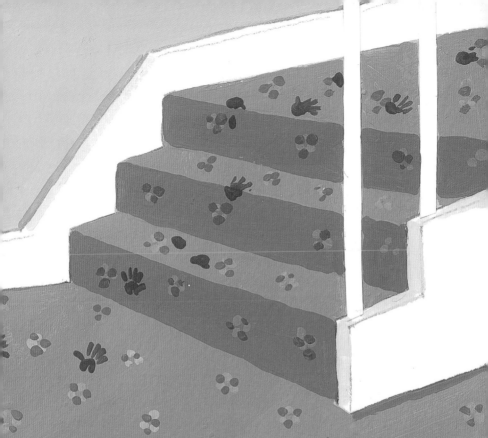

I can see jam on the stairs.

But where is baby?

9

I can see jam on the cat.

Baby is asleep
on the mat.